MOSBY
— and his —
RANGERS

*Adventures of
the Gray Ghost*

Other Books by Susan Provost Beller:

Roots for Kids: A Genealogy Guide for Young People
Cadets at War: The True Story of Teenage Heroism at the
    Battle of New Market
Woman of Independence: The Life of Abigail Adams
Medical Practices in the Civil War

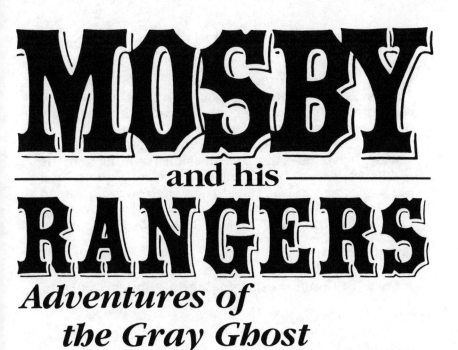

MOSBY
and his
RANGERS

Adventures of
the Gray Ghost

Susan Provost Beller

BETTERWAY BOOKS
Cincinnati, Ohio

Cover design by Rick Britton
Typography by Blackhawk Typesetting

96 95 94 93 92 5 4 3 2 1

Library of Congress Cataloging-in-Publication Data

Beller, Susan Provost.
    Mosby and his rangers : adventures of the gray ghost /
Susan Provost Beller.
        p.   cm.
    Includes bibliographical references and index.
    Summary: Describes how Colonel John Mosby and his
partisan soldiers conducted successful guerrilla warfare on
Northern troops during the Civil War.
    ISBN 1-55870-265-2 (pbk.) : $5.95
    1. Confederate States of America. Army. Virginia Cav-
alry Battalion, Forty-third — History — Juvenile literature.
2. United States — History — Civil War, 1861-1865 —
Regimental histories — Juvenile literature. 3. United States
— History — Civil War, 1861-1865 — Underground movements — Juvenile literature. 4. Guerrillas — United States
— History — 19th century — Juvenile literature. [1. Con-
federate States of America. Army. Virginia Cavalry Battalion, Forty-third — History. 2. United States — History —
Civil War, 1861-1865 — Regimental histories. 3. United
States — History — Civil War, 1861-1865 — Underground
movements. 4. Guerrillas — History — 19th century.]
I. Title.
E581.6 43rd.B45 1992
973.7'455— dc20   92-17475
                                                        CIP
                                                        AC

This book is dedicated to my son, Michael Patrick Beller, who shares with Mosby the honor of having attended Mr. Jefferson's University.

ACKNOWLEDGMENTS

As always, many "thank-yous" are necessary when a book like this is completed. My thanks to Adele H. Mitchell, one of the founders and leading movers of the Stuart-Mosby Historical Society, for a most interesting interview and for assistance in obtaining private Mosby family photographs to include here. Thanks also to Mary Ison, of the Library of Congress Prints and Photographs Division; to Don Kloster, Curator of the Division of Armed Forces History at the Smithsonian Institution; to Michael J. Winey, Curator of the Special Collections Branch of the U.S. Army Military History Institute; and to Michael Plunkett, Curator of Manuscripts, and his staff at Alderman Library, University of Virginia.

My three children, Mike, Jennie, and Sean, again offered their services as readers for this manuscript. They always have very interesting comments to offer and they seem to have a knack for catching all the things I've left unclear in my writing. My colleague in the library at Bristol Elementary School, Dee Corkins, also read this manuscript and, as always, helped to strengthen the way it reads.

My husband, Michael, should win medals for all his assistance. Not only was he my grammatical editor, he also possesses such a good background knowledge of the Civil War that he served as my encyclopedia of Civil War history. He also "heard" this book many times before it was ever written as I talked out what was to be included. Finally, he also gave me a sense of perspective when at times I began to lose sight of the fact that there were two sides to the Mosby story.

CONTENTS

Prologue

IN THE END

It was April of 1865. The Confederacy lay in ruins. The Union soldiers had won the grueling, four-year war. The South would be forced to become part of the Union again. They would have to accept the hated Lincoln as their leader. For the South, it was a time of bitterness and despair.

As the Southern troops began their surrender, one unit of Confederate troops refused to give up. On April 21, 1865, Colonel John Singleton Mosby disbanded his raiders rather than have them surrender to the Union troops.

Mosby and his unusual group of guerrilla soldiers left the field undefeated and unbowed. Not only had they been successful in their assignment to harass and delay the Union troops, but now they would leave the war without ever acknowledging defeat.

This was a war that saw the Confederacy defeated not for any lack of leadership or lack of courage. The Confederacy lost because it was worn down by the greater resources of the North. In this war that saw the brilliant leadership of Robert E. Lee and "Stonewall" Jackson, John Singleton Mosby stood out as an exceptional leader in a very different kind of war than the one Lee and Jackson fought in.

For two years, part of Virginia and Maryland was known as Mosby's Confederacy. And in this territory, no one ever stopped Mosby and his raiders. To the great frustration of Union leaders, he and his partisan band struck again and again, fighting a war the Union troops couldn't even begin to keep up with. Time after time, the North detailed men to stop his attacks. Time after time, Mosby struck their supply wagons, their horses, their communications, their railroads — and got away with it.

The story of Mosby, the "Gray Ghost," and his partisan rangers is one of the most exciting stories of the entire Civil War.

Chapter 1

MOSBY, GROWING UP A REBEL

John Singleton Mosby was born on December 6, 1833, at the home of his mother's parents in Edgemont, Powhatan County, Virginia. His father, Alfred Daniel Mosby, was a farmer in nearby Nelson County. His mother, Virginia McLaurine, had already had one other child, a baby girl, who had died. John would be frail and rather sickly himself while growing up. He would be followed in the family by several more sisters and one more brother, Willie, who would fight as one of his rangers during the war. In 1840, his father moved his growing family to Albemarle County, about four miles outside of Charlottesville. By age ten, he was attending a school for boys in Charlottesville. By sixteen, he was ready to enroll in the University of Virginia, also in Charlottesville, which he entered in the fall of 1850. There he would study Greek and mathematics and excel in both subjects.

While a student at the University, Mosby became famous in a very negative way. As the editor of his memoirs wrote: "He was convicted of unlawfully shooting a fellow student and was sentenced to a fine and imprisonment in the jail at Charlottesville. It was the case of defending the good name of a young lady and while the law was doubtless violated, public sentiment was indicated by the legislature's remitting the fine and

John Singleton Mosby as a student at the University of Virginia. (John Mosby Collections, Prints File, Manuscript Division, Special Collections Department, University of Virginia Library.)

Rotunda of the University of Virginia. John Mosby caused a scandal for the university when he shot a fellow student in March 1853. He was expelled from the university. It wasn't until 1915 that the dispute between him and the University of Virginia was resolved. (Photograph by W. Michael Beller.)

14

Pauline Clarke married Mosby in 1857. Many of Mosby's letters to his "Dearest Pauline" during the Civil War still exist. (Mosby Family Photograph.)

Three of Mosby's daughters — Virginia Stuart, Ada, and Pauline. Mosby had two small children when he left to serve in the Confederate army. His letters to Pauline mention them often and it is apparent how much he missed them. (Mosby Family Photograph.)

the governor's granting a pardon." Aristides Monteiro, who would later become a surgeon in Mosby's regiment, was a fellow student and visited Mosby shortly after he was convicted. He wrote later in his *War Reminiscences* that "Of all my University friends and acquaintances this youthful prisoner would have been the last one I would have selected with the least expectations that the world would ever hear from him again."

The experience of his own trial led to Mosby's choice of a profession. After he had expressed an interest in a career in law, the lawyer who prosecuted him loaned him some of his law books to read while in prison. The prosecutor, William Robertson, would help him along in his career choice, and they would remain friends for life. Mosby was admitted to the bar as an attorney himself in 1855.

On December 30, 1857, he married Pauline Clarke, who was the daughter of the Honorable Beverly J. Clarke, a former Congressman from Kentucky. By the time the Civil War began, he and his wife had two small children — a daughter, May Virginia, born May 10, 1859, and an infant son, Beverly. The family was living in Bristol, Virginia, where Mosby practiced law.

The Mosby who left his law practice and joined the Confederate army to defend his home state did not particularly look like a hero. He wasn't very tall and he was rather thin, not apparently someone most people would notice. Almost all the memoirs written by his men comment on how surprised they were when they first met him. James Williamson probably describes his reaction best: "I expected to see a man such as novelists picture when describing some terrible brigand chief. I was therefore somewhat surprised when one of my Companions pointed to a rather slender, but wiry look-ing young man of medium height, with light hair, keen eyes and pleasant expression ... I could scarcely believe that the slight frame before me could be that of the man who had won such military fame by his daring."

Ranger Munson, only in his teens when he became a ranger, described his reaction on seeing Mosby for the first time as "shock." After describing Mosby as "small" and "plainly attired," he goes on to write that "The total absence of visible might, the lack of swagger, the quiet demeanor of the man, all contributed to my astonishment."

As the war opened, this frail-looking lawyer from Bristol, Virginia, along with many other loyal Virginians, enlisted to defend his home state. For Mosby, his encounter with history was about to begin. And the history of the American Civil War would never be the same.

Chapter 2

MOSBY — SOLDIER

Twenty years after the Civil War ended, Mosby would write in his *Reminiscences*: "I was never half as much frightened in any fight I was in as I was on the first dress parade I conducted." In his *Memoirs*, he would be more explicit about his dislike of regular life in the Confederate army: "The experiences of my first night in camp rather tended to chill my military ardor ... camp duty was always irksome to me and I preferred being on the outposts." The kind of military genius Mosby possessed would not appear in the day-to-day life of camp in the army.

Mosby had not wanted the South to secede from the Union. He was a thoughtful, intelligent man. When he looked ahead to the effects of secession, he saw only terrible civil war — and his vision would become true. But when Virginia did vote to secede, for Mosby there was no question of what he would choose to do. He immediately joined the Confederate army as a private. "Virginia went out of the Union by force of arms, and I went with her," he wrote years later in his *Memoirs*. He had enlisted without even completing the law cases he was working on. At first he was able to remain at home, only a part-time soldier. He drilled in military skills part of the day and defended his clients the rest of the time. He would later write, as he closed up his law practice and became a full-time soldier, "I had no dream then that I would be anything more than a private soldier."

With their training completed, Mosby's unit was ordered to Richmond to receive their weapons and their orders. After a long, wet ride to Richmond, Mosby found himself equipped with a rifle and a saber and on the march to Winchester, Virginia. Mosby's cavalry unit, the Washington Mounted Rifles, was being sent to join up with (then) Lt. Colonel J.E.B. Stuart's First Virginia Cavalry. Only a few weeks later, he was involved in the first major battle of the Civil War, near Bull Run Creek in Manassas, Virginia. After the battle, which the Southern troops won, he would write to his wife, Pauline, of his feelings during the battle: "We were placed in the most trying position in which troops can be placed, to be exposed to a fire you cannot return ... There was scarcely a minute during the battle that I did not think of you and my sweet babes."

All day long, the First Virginia Cavalry sat on their horses, often under fire, waiting to be ordered into the battle. As the battle ended, they finally were given an opportunity for action. The unit was ordered to pursue the retreating Union troops. The Washington Rifles chased the Union army for about eight miles. Mosby was in a position to see all the terrible damage done by the battle, and, riding back across the battlefield that night, to hear the sounds of the wounded as they waited for medical care. He would write to Pauline that the sounds and sights of that night were "heart-rending."

For the rest of 1861 and early 1862, Mosby served with his unit. They were in no major battles, but Mosby often found himself involved in skirmishes with Union troops. He also found himself socializing with them. In August 1861, he wrote to Pauline of having some "Yankees" come to visit them under a flag of truce and stay for supper.

This portrait of Mosby was taken after the war ended. It is the last photograph of him in his uniform. (University of Virginia Library.)

In February 1862, Mosby was detailed to drive some Confederate women to safety farther behind the lines. Completing his task, he found himself having dinner with three Confederate generals. For a lowly private, this was an awe-inspiring experience. In his *Reminiscences* many years later, he would write of the experience, noting that he was with men whom he "would have regarded it as a great privilege the day before to view through a long range telescope."

Also in February, he found himself promoted to adjutant of the regiment. It was not a job he enjoyed and it was here he conducted the dress parade that he re-membered with such dread twenty years after the war. But he would not remain adjutant to the Washington Rifles much longer. In March came the opportunity that would lead to his career as a scout and would get him the active attention of General J.E.B. Stuart.

General Stuart needed to know exactly where the Union army was and what its plans were as the spring fighting opened in 1862. Mosby volunteered to find out. Taking only three men, he went behind enemy lines to see what information he could find. When he returned with the information Stuart needed, Stuart offered him any reward he wanted. Mosby wrote later: "The only reward I asked was the opportunity to do the same thing again." He would get the reward he asked for.

On June 16, 1862, he would write to Pauline, "I returned yesterday with General Stuart from the grand-est scout of the war. I not only helped to execute it, but was the first who conceived and demonstrated that it was practicable ... everybody says it's the greatest feat of this war. I never enjoyed myself so much in my life." The feat was a remarkable one and one that was the real beginning of a great team — that of Mosby and Stuart. Mosby had suggested an incredible scheme for Stuart's cavalry — to ride around the rear of the main Union army, raiding their supplies and disrupting their camps along the way. Stuart liked the scheme, and the results were everything both of them had hoped for. The Union troops, which so greatly outnumbered Stuart's small force of 1,200 cavalry, were surprised and unable to respond to so bold an attack. Stuart reported to Lee and the Confederate Secretary of War on this great exploit, giving credit to Mosby and recommending his promotion.

More important for Mosby, Stuart decided to keep him nearby and use him for more scouting missions. Mosby would always turn a mission into a success, even if the mission did not go quite as it was planned. In July, Mosby was sent on a mission that ended with his capture by Union troops. After being interrogated, he found himself a prisoner in the Old Capitol prison in Washington, D.C. By the time he was sent back as an exchanged prisoner, he had obtained information on important Union troop movements. In his typical bold style, immediately after his release, Mosby rode directly to General Robert E. Lee, Commander of the entire Confederate army, with the information he had obtained. He had never met Lee but insisted on seeing him. He wrote later that Lee "listened attentively, and after I was through called a staff officer to have a man ready to take a dispatch to General Jackson." Mosby's information changed Lee's plans and led to a successful attack by the Confederate army on the Union troops at Cedar Mountain before they could be reinforced with more men. For Mosby, it was just another bold maneuver, turning his capture into a great victory for the Confederate army.

Mosby returned to Stuart's command and continued his successful scouting activities for the remainder of 1862. As the armies of both sides moved into winter quarters, Mosby went to Stuart with a request "to stay behind for a few days with a squad of men." Knowing that Mosby had no desire just to sit around in winter camp, Stuart granted his request. With his nine men and his feeling that "I could do something with them," Mosby began the career that would make him a legend in both the North and the South.

Chapter 3

THE GRAY GHOST — TWO RAIDS

he night was clear and crisp and cold. As we came from the direction of their camp, we were mistaken for the patrol until we got upon them. The challenge of the sentinel was answered by an order to charge, and it was all over with the boys from the Green Mountains. Their surprise was so great that they forgot that they had only pistols and carbines ... They made no resistance. With these words in his *Reminiscences*, Mosby sums up his most famous raid. Mosby and his rangers provide great stories. He and his men had many exciting adventures together. Before we look at some of the details of how the rangers were organized and how their raids were planned, let's look at the most famous and most successful of Mosby's raids, the one at Fairfax Courthouse, Virginia, in March 1863. We'll also look at another success of Mosby's later in the war, at Leesburg, Virginia, and Point of Rocks, Maryland, in July 1864.

In early January 1863, Mosby, with the small group of men assigned to his command by General Stuart, began his campaign of harassing the Union troops. He was successful enough that the Union troops started sending out groups of soldiers to try to track him down. Mosby became quite good at not only escaping the troops sent to get him, but also at fighting back. A Union colonel named Percy Wyndham was very persistent in trying to capture Mosby. Worse still, he had referred to Mosby as a horse thief. Mosby decided to take his men right into the Union camp and capture Wyndham.

It was a daring and very crazy plan. They would be going into an area where there were three Union cavalry regiments, two infantry regiments, and two infantry brigades camped. Mosby and his twenty-nine men would be attempting to capture one individual in a camp that was filled with Union soldiers. Dr. Monteiro would write of Mosby's own account of the raid: "There is something so wild and desperate in piercing the very heart of a large army ... that it reads more like the creation of fiction, than the historic realities of military life."

Mosby and his men traveled the twenty-five miles to the camp where Wyndham was. The camp was located ten miles behind the Union lines. Mosby divided his men into small groups and sent them quietly to different parts of the camp. His group went to the headquarters of Brigadier General Stoughton, woke him up, and took him prisoner. One account of the story says that in waking up the general, Mosby asked him if he knew who Mosby was. The general answered that he did and asked if Mosby had been caught. Mosby told him "No" and then introduced himself.

The rangers never even had occasion to fire their guns. But in the ninety minutes they spent in camp, they had captured one Union general, two captains, thirty regular soldiers, and fifty-eight horses. Mosby admitted they could have had more horses if they had wanted. In his official report on his raid to Confederate General J.E.B. Stuart, he noted: "We left hundreds of horses in the stables and other places having no way of bringing them off as I was already encumbered with more prisoners and horses than I had men." Mosby and

Union Brigadier General Edwin Henry Stoughton was captured by Mosby in his most famous raid in March 1863. (U.S. Army Military History Institute.)

It was the success of Mosby's raid here at Fairfax Courthouse that earned him permission to organize a company of partisan raiders. (Library of Congress.)

his men had pulled off an impossible raid and neither the Union nor the Confederacy would ever be quite the same for it. There was one disappointment for Mosby, though — Colonel Wyndham had gone to Washington for the night, so Mosby did not catch his opponent.

With one raid, Mosby had become part of Southern legend. Even he realized it was a once in a lifetime event. For the Union it was a disaster. It would be a long time before Union officers in Virginia would sleep comfortably again. Union soldiers, trying to explain what had happened, talked of being attacked by 300 men. Mosby himself remembered the story that made the rounds after his raid: "There is an anecdote told of Mr. Lincoln that, when it was reported to him that Stoughton had been captured, he remarked, with characteristic humor, that he did not mind so much the loss of a general — for he could make another in five minutes — but he hated to lose the horses."

The real effect of the raid was that Mosby earned the right to organize his own company of guerrilla troops. He had proven to the Confederate leaders that there was a place for his kind of warfare. Mosby's Rangers had been born.

The second raid took place once Mosby's reputation was well established. In the spring of 1864, the Confederate troops were on the move again. This time General Jubal Early was involved in a daring attempt to sneak into Maryland and attack Washington, D.C. directly. Mosby's job was to cut railroad and telegraph lines between Harper's Ferry, West Virginia and Washington, D.C. This he did, crossing over to Point of Rocks, Maryland, under heavy fire. Ranger Williamson notes that "The telegraph operator ran off and hid in the mountains, where he remained until we had all left." Upon returning and rigging equipment to send a short message, the operator, according to Williamson, sent a message saying "the devil was to pay generally" in describing the damage they had done.

Mosby and his rangers stayed for two days, collecting three wagonloads of Union goods, which were desperately needed in the South. They took shoes, cloth, bonnets, food, and cigars while they were there. They crossed back into Virginia, and Mosby sent a good part of his forces home to bring back the material they had taken. Mosby and his remaining 150 men stayed to create what havoc they could.

But now Mosby learned that there was a Union force somewhat larger than his out looking for him. He shadowed these Union troops as they headed down towards Washington, D.C. from Leesburg, Virginia. Finally he circled around them while they took a break and took up a position in front of them. Mosby and his men charged the troops. The fighting between the two groups was brutal. Some of it, like the fighting between the Union leader, Major Forbes, and Mosby, was hand-to-hand. Munson remembered: "It was a mass of struggling, cursing maniacs, each striving to slay his antagonist." Williamson remembered the scene as the battle ended: "The ground was strewn with guns, pistols, blankets and equipment of all kinds; dead and wounded were lying around; horses, wounded and maddened with pain and fright, dashed wildly over the battleground."

Mosby and his men had been successful once again. In the words of Ranger J. Marshall Crawford, "This was a proud day for Mosby. He had vanquished, in fact annihilated, with one hundred and fifty men, two hundred and fifty men picked out of three regiments for their bravery and fighting qualities, who had been out three days looking for Mosby." Mosby and his partisans captured almost fifty prisoners, including Major Forbes. They took one hundred Union horses and left twelve Union soldiers dead and another thirty-seven wounded. Mosby and his men had only one death with several others only slightly wounded. Mosby's legend continued to grow.

There is a sequel to the story of the skirmish between Mosby and Forbes in Leesburg. After the Civil War, Forbes and Mosby became close friends and remained friends until their deaths many years later.

Chapter 4

ORGANIZING THE RANGERS

In his *Memoirs*, Mosby writes of his first partisan assignment from Stuart. He was given fifteen men to work with and he admits: "It looked as though I was leading a forlorn hope, but I was never discouraged." From the beginning, Mosby knew what it was he wanted to achieve. "My purpose," he wrote, "was to threaten and harass the enemy on the border and in this way compel him to withdraw troops from his front to guard the line of the Potomac and Washington." His goal was always to keep the Union troops busy so that they could not be spared to join the regular army fighting on the front lines. It was a job for which Mosby was well-suited.

To achieve his goal, he would work with a unique group of soldiers. They would give him almost unheard of loyalty. He, in turn, would lead them on adventures that would be the envy of the soldiers in the regular army.

Mosby knew why soldiers were attracted to his battalion. In his *Reminiscences* he wrote: "The true secret was that it was a fascinating life, and its attractions far more than counterbalanced its hardships and dangers." The editor of Mosby's *Memoirs*, Charles Russell, adds his own comments: "Attracted by the chance of booty and desire for adventure without the irksome duties of camp life, brave and dashing spirits were

Mosby (standing, second from left) posing with some of his rangers. (Library of Congress.)

drawn to Mosby's battalion until the fifteen men ... became five companies, regularly mustered into the Confederate service." In actual fact, Russell's count was too low. By the end of the Civil War, those fifteen men had actually become eight companies of about one hundred men each.

Many of Mosby's men wrote memoirs of their days as partisan rangers. Almost every one of them attempts to explain why they chose the partisan life over that of a regular soldier in the Confederate army. J. Marshall Crawford explained his choice this way: "The life of a guerrilla is a dangerous one, but it has its charms. Its independence and freedom from restraint, and, above all, the opportunity for bold and daring actions, which carry with them personal renown, makes this life far preferable to a position in the regular army."

Dr. Aristides Monteiro, who had been a student at the University of Virginia with Mosby before the war, was serving in the Confederate army when he met his former classmate in Richmond in 1864. Mosby invited him to join his regiment and arranged for Monteiro's transfer. Monteiro explains his acceptance of this new part by saying, "The peculiar fascination of partisan life, added to the brilliant record he had already made as an independent leader, his daring adventures and successful raids, mingled with a charming spirit of romance and the capture of dazzling spoils, excited the strongest emotions and kindled the liveliest ambition in the hearts of the old soldiers of the regular service." Dr. Monteiro was an unusual member of Mosby's battalion since he came by transfer from the regular Confederate army. Most of the rangers did not. Many of the partisans were former soldiers, retired from the army because of injuries that made them unable to keep up with the demands of army life. Some of the rangers were older men, too old for the regular army but able to help out while living at home either through gathering information or participating in raids.

Most of Mosby's men, however, were young men who lived in Virginia and were from the area known as Mosby's Confederacy. This area included Fauquier, Loudoun, Fairfax, and Prince William Counties in the northern part of the state. Of non-Virginians, Marylanders were the next biggest group.

Many of Mosby's "men" were really only boys. The youngest was only fourteen. John W. Munson, only fifteen himself in 1861 when the war began, said in his *Reminiscences of a Mosby Guerrilla*: "What Mosby liked best was youth. He agreed with Napoleon that boys make the best soldiers ... While on a raid they were always as light-hearted as school boys at recess." Munson estimated that fifty or sixty of the six hundred rangers at any time were boys who had run away from home to fight with Mosby. They might be too young to enlist in the regular army but they were ideal for Mosby's rangers.

Mosby would make use of anyone who could help. He even used soldiers recovering from their wounds in the hospital. Mosby wrote about the advantages of using these men. They could spend their nights raiding, but the next day, when the Union troops tried to find them, they would be convalescing in the hospital.

It is hard to know how many men were part of Mosby's group during the last two years of the Civil War. Some books say 800, others over 1,900. Writers do seem to agree that there were six or seven hundred active members of the battalion at the end of the Civil War in April 1865. One reason it is hard to count them is because they never all gathered together at once to go into battle.

Mosby's men actually belonged to the 43rd Battalion of Virginia Cavalry. Mosby didn't get official permission to organize his first company of rangers until March 23, 1863 in a letter from General Lee. His most famous raid, his capture of General Stoughton at Fairfax Courthouse, happened before there was officially even a group of partisan rangers. He was authorized by General Stuart to organize a company of men on March 25, 1863, but the actual formation of this "Company A" did not take place until June 10th. By October 1st of the same year, he had so many men he needed to divide the group, and "Company B" was formed. A year later, the battalion contained seven companies. In January 1865, the battalion became a regiment under Mosby's general command. The men were divided into two separate battalions commanded by William H. Chapman and Adolphus "Dolly" Richards, two of Mosby's best rangers. By the end of the Civil War, there were eight companies organized into the two battalions — a much, much larger group than the original fifteen men who made the first raid with Mosby in early 1863.

Reading the memoirs of Mosby's men, what comes across strongly is the loyalty and devotion Mosby's men felt for him. This loyalty was the glue that held together this very different group of men. John Alexander wrote of Mosby's leadership: "His wonderful genius manifested itself as much in understanding and handling his men as in recognizing and rising to the opportunities which came to him." He continued with a discussion of Mosby's concern for his men and his sympathy for their needs.

Ranger J. Marshall Crawford wrote that "He was warm-hearted ... never known to forsake a friend in time of need." "Dolly" Richards wrote of "his skill in finding out genius in others, and his promptness in calling it into action." Dr. Monteiro voiced this opinion: "Virginia can claim no truer son or braver soldier, nor has she ever given birth to a more honest and faithful man than John Singleton Mosby."

Ranger John Munson brought all the aspects of the feelings Mosby's men had for him together when he wrote that "Mosby's correct estimate of men, his absolute freedom from jealousy and selfishness, his unerring judgment at critical moments, his devotion to his men, his eternal vigilance, his unobtrusive bravery and his exalted sense of personal honor, all combined to create in the mind and heart of those who served him a sort of hero worship." With this loyalty and devotion from his followers, it is no wonder that Mosby and his partisans are still remembered today.

Chapter 5

THE DAILY LIFE OF THE RANGERS

We used neither carbines, nor sabres, but all the men carried a pair of Colt pistols. We did not pay for them but the U.S. Government did. With this funny quip, Mosby gave some idea of how the rangers lived from day to day. He also wrote more seriously on the same subject: "We lived on the country where we operated and drew nothing from Richmond except the gray jackets my men wore. We were mounted, armed, and equipped entirely off the enemy."

Mosby and his men, although part of the Confederate army, operated separately from the army in every way. They were responsible for providing their own food, supplies, guns, transportation, and housing. Dr. Monteiro explained their living arrangements, writing: "Our soldiers were quartered in squads of four to ten men at each private residence, mostly throughout the county of Fauquier." Living in private homes proved exciting for everyone involved, especially as the Union troops became more insistent in their searches for Mosby. Dr. Monteiro had only been with the partisans for a short time when he found himself escaping by lying on the frozen roof of the house where he was staying, wearing only his nightclothes, hoping the Union soldiers would not find him. He noted that "almost every dwelling occupied by Mosby's men was provided with trap-doors and other convenient subterranean hiding places."

The people who housed the partisans also provided them with food, but the rangers were expected to obtain their own horses and other supplies. Ranger John W. Munson wrote that the Southerners were glad to have Mosby's men living with them and gave them whatever they needed. The rangers repaid the civilians' kindnesses. Munson wrote that "whenever we made a successful raid, we made it a point to repay the farmers and country people whose bounty we enjoyed, in live stock and supplies."

The weapon of choice for Mosby's battalion was the Colt pistol. Mosby himself later wrote: "We did more than any other body of men to give the Colt pistol its great reputation." The rangers, often shown in drawings and paintings charging with their sabers, did not, in fact, use them. Mosby would not allow their use because "the sabre and lance may have been very good weapons in the days of chivalry ... But certainly the sabre is of no use against gunpowder." Mosby was a very practical leader who chose for his men the weapon he felt was most suited to the job he would have them doing. His men also did not carry rifles, since most of their fighting was at such short-range that rifles would not have been very effective. Munson would write about the Colt pistols: "These weapons were extremely deadly and effective ... Long and frequent practice had made every man in the Command a good shot."

The most important "equipment" for the ranger was his horse. The men usually tried to have two, for as Munson noted, "the work was too hard for one horse." He said that Mosby himself had six horses at one point during the war. The horses were stabled at the house where the ranger was living.

One other piece of "equipment" needs to be noted because it was much debated after the war ended — that

This jacket of Mosby's is on display in the Smithsonian Institution's National Museum of American History in the Armed Forces History section. (Smithsonian Institution.)

is, the uniforms of Mosby's men. Many Union soldiers claimed that Mosby and his men were able to pull off their great deeds only by disguising themselves by wearing blue uniforms. It is a charge strongly denied by Mosby and by those of his partisans who later wrote about their adventures. In his *Reminiscences*, Mosby wrote: "I always wore the Confederate uniform, with the insignia of my rank. So did my men. So any success ... cannot be accounted for on the theory that it was accomplished through disguise." Munson called the charge "ridiculous," noting that "we were always in the enemy's country where a Southern soldier caught dressed in a blue uniform would have been treated to a swift court-martial and shot as a spy." He goes on to state: "I never knew, nor did I ever hear, of any man in our Command wearing a blue uniform under any circumstances."

Many of Mosby's men later wrote how they enjoyed the relaxed discipline of being part of the 43rd Battalion. There were never any drills, parades, or other camp-life duties. They didn't have to pitch tents or cook their own meals. There were no forced marches. They even were allowed to call their officers (except Mosby himself) by their first names. It was an easy life compared to the drudgery of the common soldier's daily existence. This, of course, was part of the appeal of the partisan life. John H. Alexander, a former member of Mosby's command whose memoirs are more exaggerated and less accurate than those of other former partisans, shares this observation: "The truth is, we were an undisciplined lot ... when not under command of the officers, each man was his own commander, commissary, quartermaster and everything else. He was dependent on his own resources for supplies and his own wits for safety." Alexander's memoir glories in the daredevil tactics and the unmilitary behavior of the men.

However, he also noted the personal control that Mosby had over the command when he wrote that "no one cared to provoke a second time his trenchant disapproval." Under the wrong leader, this band of partisans could have been a disaster. With Mosby in command, the men stayed under control.

Ranger Munson said it best when he wrote: "We did not practice anything usually required of a soldier, and yet withal there was not another body of men in the army under better or more willing control of their leader." There was only one punishment for any disobedience or variation from Mosby's orders, and that was being removed from the battalion and returned to the Confederate army. Dr. Monteiro wrote: "To be ordered back into the regular service was regarded by every man in the Forty-third battalion of Virginia Cavalry, as intolerable punishment and eternal disgrace ... Every man knew that the slightest suspicion of dishonesty, or cowardice, would consign him at once to the disgrace of expulsion." It was a severe punishment for these partisans who loved the high adventure and lack of military discipline of this command. It gave Mosby life and death control over them. And it made them obey him.

Chapter 6

THE RANGERS — TACTICS

With six to eight hundred men living at houses throughout a large part of Northern Virginia, there had to be some sort of system to call men together when they were needed. Mosby wrote that he "rarely rested for more than one day at a time. As soon as I knew of a point offering a chance for successful attack, I gathered my men together and struck a blow." The most important part of his strategy had to be information. He continually sent out groups of rangers to scout the territory.

Former ranger James J. Williamson wrote that he felt Mosby's success as a strategist came from "the selection of skillful and intelligent guides and scouts — men familiar with the section of the country in which he operated — knowing all the little roads and cowpaths; who could creep through the dense undergrowth or dark ravines like foxes." He also had the cooperation of the civilians living in Union-occupied territory, who provided information. Finally, Mosby made it a point to interview every prisoner they took, writing that "in this way together with information gained from citizens, I obtained a pretty accurate knowledge of conditions in the enemy's camps."

Mosby's actual raids did not involve many of his men at one time. He always wanted a small group so that he could slip in and out without being caught. Williamson

John Singleton Mosby in the uniform of a Confederate major. With the establishment of his command, he was promoted to major effective March 26, 1863. (Library of Congress.)

wrote that there were certain places where they would gather and usually they would have set a time and place to meet again. But he noted Mosby could always call the men together using "couriers" and, on a few hours' notice, Mosby could always have a large enough group ready to go.

It was Mosby himself — or, later on when the unit had grown, the company commander — who planned their raids. Munson wrote that "Mosby never took anyone into his confidence." He gave an example of a time when Mosby invited him to ride with him as he planned the next day's raid. They rode together for twenty miles and "not once did he look at me, nor one word did he utter. He was planning one of those sensational raids of his, which, before the next sunset, startled Washington and kept the Federal commanders in a flutter for many days afterward. I thought my tongue would become paralyzed from long disuse." Even when he gathered the men at their rendezvous point, Mosby often didn't share with them the goal of the night's activity. They first followed him, and when they neared the attack point he would give them just enough information to carry out his instructions. It was an effective way of operating for Mosby. It also shows the level of trust his men had in him.

When a raid was completed, the men would separate and head back to their own "homes." Only enough of the group to escort the prisoners and horses that had been captured would stay together. Union troops coming to pursue would find no one to chase. In time, the Union pursuers became so persistent that the men had to give up their "safe houses" and move to various caves in the Blue Ridge Mountains. Even then, the men dispersed and gathered only when they were needed. It was this tactic of Mosby's that would drive the Union pursuers crazy.

The other strategy that Mosby used was to attack at night whenever possible. Munson wrote that Mosby preferred night raids "as he held that sleeping men are easy to surround, and that it required at least five minutes for an awakened soldier to get in shape to fight." Using this strategy, Mosby and his partisans would often enter a camp, take some prisoners and horses, and escape without ever having to use their weapons.

Mosby also used boldness as an effective tactic. J. Marshall Crawford gave an account of a raid on a supply wagon train that captured three wagons, carried out while a Union brigade was marching by them, and noted: "On this raid not a pistol was fired, while we captured and destroyed seventy-five thousand dollars worth of property." The Union leaders just could not believe that Mosby would attack them in such an open manner.

45

Several of the memoirs praise Mosby's boldness and his ability to carry off exciting raids that almost sound foolhardy in their descriptions. What these accounts often neglect to mention is that the success of these raids was not just luck, but rather the sound planning Mosby put into them. Munson noted that Mosby "never lost his self-possession; never got rattled" and "it was impossible to confuse him." The task taken on by Mosby required a leader with very special qualities and a great deal of nerve. Mosby had these qualities in great quantity. The raids were logically planned and well executed by a man who knew his goal and understood how it must be achieved. In his *Reminiscences*, Mosby wrote his definition of this goal: "It was safer for me, and greater results could be secured by being the aggressor and striking the enemy at unguarded points. I could thus compel him to guard a hundred points while I could select any one of them for attack ... The military value of a partisan's work is not measured by the amount of property destroyed, or the number of men killed or captured, but by the number he keeps watching." Mosby kept the entire Union army stationed in Northern Virginia watching.

Chapter 7

TARGETS

To destroy supply trains, to break up the means of conveying intelligence and thus isolating an army from its base, as well as its different corps from each other, to confuse their plans by capturing despatches, are the objects of partisan war. With these words written in his *Reminiscences*, Mosby stated the objective and targets for his successful guerrilla operations in 1863 and 1864.

Many people during the war, on both sides, and many after the war would criticize Mosby's use of partisan warfare. Partisan guerrilla warfare was not commonly used as a tactic at that time. Many people saw it as less than honorable. But for Mosby there was never any question that partisan warfare was a perfectly good (and also a most effective) way of fighting the enemy. He defended himself and his rangers with the words: "One of the most effective ways of impeding the march of an army is by cutting off its supplies; and this is just as legitimate as to attack it in line of battle."

The targets of the rangers were all the ones that could cause the most trouble for the Union troops. Especially popular were attacks on supply wagon trains, because then the rangers could bring back something for themselves and for the people who sheltered them. Dr. Monteiro described one such raid: "There was generally a strong attraction — a sort of affinity — existing between the partisan battalion and a wagon train. Our boys waited, like a cat awaits the appearance of a mouse, until the coveted and tempting prize approached within short musket range, when, at a given signal, a rapid charge was ordered upon the devoted teamsters."

Sutlers' wagons gave an even higher reward because, as Ranger Munson wrote, the sutler "was a traveling retail general store, with a saloon attachment sometimes, and sometimes a bakery and confectionery to boot ... The supply of stuff they had was simply bewildering." The sutlers were civilians who followed after the armies to sell the soldiers items that were not usually supplied to the soldiers by the army.

While the attacks on the sutlers' wagons were more fun, it was the attack on military supply wagons that caused more damage to the armies. Ranger Williamson wrote in his memoirs of several attacks on supply trains. He told of one in October 1863 in which Mosby and fifty of his men went after a large wagon train guarded by two Union infantry regiments. Mosby divided his force of fifty into three groups. One group was in charge of stopping the wagons; another unhitched the horses and mules. The third group stood ready to assist. By the time the job was finished, they had captured two hundred mules and forty horses and Williamson notes, "not a shot was fired." He wrote of another raid the next month in which they set the wagons on fire, "presenting a picture of war well worthy of an artist's pencil."

Another favorite target of Mosby's was the railroads and the telegraph lines running alongside them. He saw these as a "weak point" in the Union army's rear. Ranger Williamson provided a great description of an attack on a railroad in May 1863 at Catlett's Station, Virginia:

Railroads were favorite targets for Mosby raids. By attacking them, he could disrupt communications and the movement of supplies by the Union Army. Often the rails were heated by igniting the pile of railroad ties under them and then bent into odd shapes so they could not be used again. (Library of Congress.)

"After cutting the telegraph wire, a rail was unfastened and a wire attached to it, extended some distance from the road where the patrols would not observe it, while a man concealed behind a tree stood ready to draw the rail out of place as soon as the engine approached, throwing it off the track."

One of the most famous railroad attacks by Mosby's men was what is known as the "Greenback Raid." This occurred in October 1864. Mosby and a group of eighty of his men tore up track about ten miles west of Harper's Ferry, West Virginia. Then they hid themselves and waited for the train. Ranger Munson described the scene as the train reached the section of track where the rails had been removed. "There was a flash of yellow light in the deep cut, and with a snort that was almost human the engine and entire train proceeded to rush off the track and turn over against the side of the cut on the side of the curve, where it brought up [stopped] jangling and groaning." When Mosby's men boarded the train, they received a welcome surprise. On board the train were Union Majors, the Paymasters of General Sheridan's army, carrying with them the payroll money for the whole army. For Mosby's men, who shared the wealth, it was an incredible discovery.

Several memoirs of the rangers note that Mosby did not take his share when the rangers divided up their plunder from a raid. Mosby's men, however, were often criticized for keeping things they had captured, and the Greenback Raid would be responsible for many of the charges that they were simply common thieves. Mosby defended them strongly when he wrote: "It must not be thought that the habit of appropriating the enemy's goods was peculiar to my men — through all ages it has been the custom of war." The partisans were also criticized for the fact that the trains they derailed, including this one, often had civilian passengers, including women, on board. Again Mosby stated his defense firmly: "People who travel on a railroad in a country where military operations are going on take the risk of all these accidents of war."

All these targets had the advantage of causing maximum confusion for the Union army. John Munson wrote that they made it "necessary for the Federal troops to guard every wagon train, railroad bridge and camp ... thousands of soldiers were kept from service at the front because of Mosby's activity." He boasts: "General Grant at one time reported that seventeen thousand of his men were engaged in keeping Mosby from attacking his weak points, and thus away from active service on the firing line."

Chapter 8

COWBELLS AND OTHER STORIES

Every affair in which Mosby and his men figured had in it something novel, something romantic, something which is worth telling, according to Ranger John Munson. The stories are what have kept the memories of John Singleton Mosby and his men alive — stories like the one about one of Mosby's men who sneaked into a Union camp to take Union horses. To disguise himself, he wore a cowbell around his neck and crawled into the camp on his hands and knees. J. Marshall Crawford told the story of this escapade, noting the reaction of the Union troops to this action "which so provoked them that the commanding officer ordered the bells to be taken off every cow in the neighborhood for ten miles around."

The stories are always of bold and daring actions. There is the one that John Alexander tells of a time when Mosby took five men and went scouting to find the location of the Union patrol before they began a raid. Stopping in the road, they saw the patrol approaching them. They waited, and when the patrol approached and asked who they were, according to Alexander, Mosby replied: "'Friends, with the countersign'... with the best Yankee twang that he could improvise." When challenged, Mosby bluffed and told them to send one man forward. When the Union man approached, "the Colonel said to him in a low, terribly distinct voice, as he leveled

Shortly after his promotion, Mosby was very seriously wounded and only managed to escape by hiding out in the woods. This picture was taken while he was still recovering from that wound. (University of Virginia Library.)

his revolver at him: 'Give the alarm, and you are a dead man. I am Mosby.'" The Union rider assured his fellow soldiers that all was in order, and as they came forward, Mosby took them prisoner. It was a typical Mosby move and, as often happened, it brought him success.

Ranger "Dolly" Richards, who was Mosby's second in command, relates the story of another bold raid on the part of the rangers. He tells of a decision to attack a supply train consisting of 150 wagons. In full view of Union cavalry only one-quarter mile away, Mosby, working with a large group of 250 men this time, sent two companies of his men seventy-five yards away from the train. The men set up as if for artillery practice and fired right into the Union cavalry. As Richards noted: "Of course the Federals [Union] observed all these maneuvers, but were misled by their very boldness; they never imagined but what this new force was a part of their own army." In fact, when fired upon, the Union troops, "supposing it had been fired in that direction through mistake, hastily prepared to move beyond range." With the Union troops now in disarray, "the rebel yell was raised, and the squadron dashed at the Federals, scattering them in every direction." The result for Mosby's men was another success. They had captured 300 prisoners and hundreds of mules and horses, and burned the supply train.

What makes for such great reading in the various memoirs and reminiscences of Mosby's men is the ability of the rangers to look back and laugh at some of the things that happened to them. John Munson makes the point that "Very few of the fights of Mosby's men were pitched battles. Most of them were little affairs hardly worth writing about. Yet they were part of the almost daily experience of some of the men." He then goes on to recount some of his own little adventures. He even includes an account of himself being captured one day by about twenty Union soldiers.

Mosby's men had a reputation for "going through" their prisoners — searching them and taking for themselves anything valuable. Munson wrote that when the Union troops went through him, "the baubles and splendors of guerilla life disappeared." But he writes this account with great respect for his attackers (and also with great humor!): "Before I had time to make the slightest protest, one fellow sat me down abruptly, put his foot on me, and relieved me of my boots in a most startling and finished manner. Talk about Mosby's men going through a man! There was not a man in our command who could swoop down and capture a pair of boots like the man who took mine!"

The stories go on and on, and it is impossible even to begin to include a small part of them here. But there is one story that is so incredible that it must be told. It is a story told about and by Mosby himself, and it took place in 1864. Mosby was returning to his men from a meeting near Richmond, Virginia, and he stopped at a home for dinner. While he was eating with the family, a group of Union soldiers surrounded the home. In the fighting that took place, Mosby was shot and very severely wounded.

Mosby's own memoirs recall: "I determined to play the part of a dying man ... pulled off my coat, on which were the insignia of my rank, tucked it away under the bureau so that no one could see it, and then lay down with my head towards the bureau ... A [Union] doctor examined the wound and said it was mortal ... They left the room hurriedly, after stripping me of my boots and trousers, evidently supposing that a dead man would have no use for them."

Mosby's own account leaves out some of the details. The people with whom he was dining claimed not to know him, saying he had just stopped and requested a meal. Mosby, when questioned, gave a false name. The Union soldiers took the papers from his coat, which identified him, but did not bother reading them until they returned to camp.

Mosby himself supposedly felt at the time that his wound (his seventh!) was probably mortal. When the Union troops left, Mosby, despite the pain and loss of blood, insisted he be moved since he knew that when his papers were read, the troops would realize who he was and return for him. Ranger Crawford wrote that he was moved by ox-cart to a home about one and one-half miles away, and just in time because, "Ere Mosby had reached Mr. Glasscock's, the enemy were back to Mr. Lake's for their prize but the bird had flown."

Dr. Monteiro's account agrees with the ox-cart but says Mosby was transported to a place in the woods where he "carefully concealed himself with leaves and brush," knowing that every house in the area would be searched once the Union troops realized who he was. Dr. Monteiro says not only every house was searched but also "every well, ice-house, barnyard, and chicken coop" while "Mosby rested quietly under his pile of leaves and brushwood."

It is hard to separate out the true facts from this legend, but whether or not all the details are true, it is a *great* story. It's also a story that makes a reader understand exactly why Ranger Williamson would write about Mosby: "Cool in danger, quick to think and practical in carrying-out his ideas — these were the qualities which aided materially in his success."

Chapter 9

SILENT SUPPORT

Partisan warfare couldn't succeed without the support of the civilian population living in the area. Mosby knew this, as well as knowing that he had that support. The Union military leadership also knew this, and their recognition of this fact led to a war of revenge against the civilians who lived in Mosby's Confederacy. We will look at the Union war against the civilians later. For now, let's look at the assistance the civilians provided to Mosby and his men.

Major John Scott, in his memoirs of life as a part of the rangers, compared Mosby to Robin Hood and Francis Marion, the "Swamp Fox" of the Revolutionary War. But he notes that those earlier partisan leaders had places to hide their men. Northern Virginia, being mostly open country without large forests or swamps, left Mosby with only one alternative. Scott wrote that Mosby "finds security in dispersion among a friendly and chivalrous people. With them the members of the battalion live as boarders and friends."

Every one of the memoirs speaks of the support received from the civilian population. Ranger Alexander wrote that, "The loyal, generous people of Fauquier and Loudoun opened their hearts as well as their homes to us." "Dolly" Richards spoke of the "old Virginia families, who were loyal and true to the Southern cause ... neither danger nor want could tempt their betrayal."

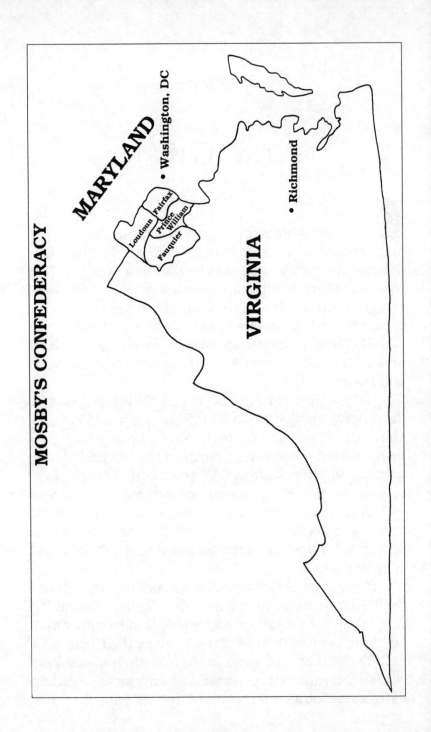

MOSBY'S CONFEDERACY

MARYLAND

Washington, DC

Loudoun

Fairfax

Prince William

Fauquier

VIRGINIA

Richmond

John Munson discusses their loyalty in a slightly different light. He agrees they were supporting the South and were glad to do so. However, he noted that these people knew they were living in disputed territory and were often behind enemy lines. Munson felt that their assistance to Mosby and his men was "also to have the protection which the presence of the Partisans afforded them."

Mosby was more than just their protector. Civil government had broken down in Northern Virginia as the war went on. Mosby served as the civilians' political leader and legal system. John Munson wrote: "The people looked to Mosby to make the necessary laws and to enforce them, and no country before, during or since the war was ever better governed."

Munson is not the only one of the rangers who felt Mosby made an excellent military governor. "Dolly" Richards wrote that "his civil administration became as remarkable for its prudence and justice as his military leadership was for magnanimity and dash."

James Williamson presented a more objective picture of Mosby law. He remembered that "'Mosby's Men' performed the duties of police as well as soldiers, and were the sole guardians of the territory." Mosby himself had the role of "military ruler" and "judge" and "not only kept the lawless element in check, but also settled differences between individuals without the tedious process of litigation, and without fear or favor." Every memoir credits Mosby's legal background with helping him to rule fairly and according to law as it had been practiced before the war.

Dr. Monteiro, Mosby's old friend from his University of Virginia days, would state it most bluntly, calling Mosby's power "arbitrary" and writing that Mosby was "a civil power of unquestioned authority over the several counties known at the time as 'Mosby's Confederacy'... He settled all disputes, and his decisions admitted no appeal." Mosby was, in effect, a dictator in those last two years of the Civil War. It was fortunate for the people of his kingdom that he was a fair one.

Not all the people living in Mosby's Confederacy supported his actions. Mosby assessed a tax on people living in the area, and one group of people gave the rangers continuing problems in collecting it. The Quaker population of Loudoun County refused to pay Mosby's tax. Dr. Monteiro was put in charge of a detail to collect the tax from the area. He remembered: "In reply to a direct and civil question, the old gentleman asked if we belonged to that infernal band of freebooters, cutthroats and thieves commanded by the rebel highwayman, Mosby." The man grudgingly quartered the group for the night, but the next day Mosby's men found that the Quaker "had betrayed us by sending a message to General Hancock ... had informed the enemy ... that we were robbing the people of Loudoun county."

The Quakers would continue to give Mosby and his men problems, as would other individuals. However, the picture history gives us is of a population dedicated to the Southern cause and willing to risk their homes and their lives to support it. For these people, the Union army was a foreign invader and Mosby represented their one chance to fight back.

Chapter 10

THE UNION GETS MAD

The major-general commanding, desires that you send two parties of cavalry, of 60 or 70 men, to scout and beat up thoroughly the county in the vicinity of the Orange and Alexandria Railroad ... No mercy need be shown to bushwhackers. These guerrillas must be destroyed. These orders from Union Chief of Staff J.H. Taylor, dated August 4, 1863, show some of the frustration the Union leadership was facing from Mosby's raids just five months into the career of the rangers.

Ever since the raid on Fairfax Courthouse and the capture of General Stoughton, the Union troops had been trying to stop Mosby. Mosby's tactics, however, proved unstoppable in this early part of the rangers' career. Mosby had begun his attacks in January 1863, but at first he was little more than a nuisance to the Union army. Colonel Percy Wyndham and his 5th New Jersey Cavalry unit were given orders to capture the small band of men.

By February 4, 1863, Mosby, still working as a scout under Stuart, would report his successful annoyance of the Union troops: "I have harassed them so much that they do not keep their pickets over a half mile from camp." There was only one obstacle in Mosby's way — Colonel Wyndham, who kept trying to stop them. Mosby's attack on Fairfax Courthouse had as its goal the capture

John Singleton Mosby as a lieutenant colonel. He was promoted by General Lee on February 6, 1864. (U.S. Army Military History Institute.)

of Wyndham. But, as noted earlier, Wyndham was not in camp that night, and Mosby caught himself a different prize.

Mosby continued his attacks on the Union camps. The Union troops continued their futile attempts to stop him. On March 31, 1863, about 150 men of the 1st Vermont Cavalry had probably their best chance at stopping Mosby early in his career. They caught Mosby and about sixty of his men camping out at a farm owned by the Miskel family. The rangers were exhausted, asleep, and unprepared for an attack. It should have been an easy victory for the Vermont cavalry. Ranger Munson would write later that "never before or after had the federal troops such another chance to secure Mosby and wipe out his men." The Vermonters charged and were stopped; then Mosby charged them, and they fled. Mosby lost one man killed; the Vermonters lost nine killed, fifteen wounded, and eighty-two captured, according to Mosby's report. It was a terrible rout for the Vermonters. Mosby's report noted: "The Yankees, never dreaming of our assuming the offensive, terrified at the yells of the men as they dashed on, broke and fled in every direction."

Mosby had learned a lesson this night that would make it even harder for any Union troops seeking him later. As he wrote in his report: "I confess, that on this occasion I had not taken sufficient precautions to guard against surprise." It was not a mistake he would repeat.

The Union troops would continue their attempts to stop Mosby. At times they would have their small victories. In May 1863, Mosby's men, badly outnumbered in a fight, would even break and run themselves. Mosby would be forced to report a situation where "there was no alternative left me but retreat." Despite their small successes, the Union never really succeeded in their ultimate goal of stopping Mosby's attacks. Mosby's men just faded away between raids and came back at them again and again.

Despite the Union orders of August 4th, by November 5, 1863, the Union leadership would have to write: "The loss in officers and men stationed in this corps at the hands of guerrillas during the past few days demands the careful attention of all to prevent a recurrence in the future." Two weeks later, Colonel J.P. Taylor would report, "The guerrillas around Warrenton are very troublesome, always attacking my pickets after nightfall."

By June 9, 1864, the Union military leaders would find it necessary to issue special regulations to the troops to "Guard against surprises." In August, orders were given for Union troops to escort all trains running through the Winchester, Virginia area. On August 14, 1864, Major William Beardsley of the Sixth New York Cavalry would be forced to report a Mosby attack on the supply train his men were escorting: "A disgraceful panic ensued resulting in the entire destruction of the Reserve Brigade's train and a portion of ours."

On August 16, 1864, Captain E.P. McKinney of the Reserve Brigade reported similar news of the destruction of his supply train. He also noted that "the guards who accompanied us, as far as I could see, threw down their arms and ran away without firing a shot." Mosby and his men had been harassing the Union troops since January 1863. Twenty months later, the local Union command's frustration level must have been extremely high. In all that time, they had fought back. They had won some skirmishes against Mosby. But the field was definitely his. It would take a special kind of Union leader to change all this — one who thought the same way Mosby did.

Chapter 11

THE UNION'S REVENGE

Beginning in September 1864, Mosby and his men finally met an enemy who used the same kind of tactics they employed. The result was the first real setback for Mosby and his rangers. Major Scott wrote after the war that Union Captain Blazer "appeared to be ever in the saddle, and was constantly turning up where he was least expected and least desired. Such was his activity that scouts and furloughed soldiers never felt safe within the enemy's lines, or in that broad neutral border which separates the hostile forces." It is amusing to read this description of a Union soldier by one of Mosby's men. Scott's complaints sound very much like those of the Union military leaders speaking of Mosby.

Blazer felt he understood Mosby and his methods. His attacks would be modeled on Mosby's own attacks. His men would have to move swiftly; they would raid at night when necessary. James Williamson noted another factor in Blazer's planning that would prove a problem for the rangers: "Captain Blazer ... by his humane and kindly treatment ... had so disarmed our citizens that instead of fleeing on his approach and notifying all soldiers, thus giving them a chance to escape, but little notice was taken of him." In other words, because Blazer was treating the local citizens kindly, they didn't flee and thus warn Mosby when the Union troops approached.

With Mosby's men not being warned, many of them were caught by Blazer and his Scouts.

His tactics would pay off. On September 4, 1864, Captain Richard Blazer and his one hundred Scouts caught a group of seventy of Mosby's men resting in the woods after a raid. James Williamson was one of the rangers resting that afternoon after picket duty. He wrote: "I did not imagine there was an enemy on our side of the river and thought the only danger would be from the other side ... pickets could give us ample warning." Williamson took a nap only to awaken to the sound of rifle fire. He was shot as he mounted his horse but managed to escape after being pursued. Williamson wrote that Mosby was furious when he heard the news, telling the men: "'You let the Yankees whip you? I'll get hoop skirts for you!'" This was a most unusual reaction for the cool, calculating Mosby.

John Munson gives a different picture of Mosby's response, claiming that Mosby never spoke of Blazer "until he finally ordered Major Richards to go over to the Valley and wipe him from the map." Munson stated that until then the rangers "made no special attempts to capture him nor any special pains to keep out of his way."

For whatever reason, Mosby ordered no raids at all for the next two weeks. Captain Blazer must have wondered whether perhaps he had successfully frightened Mosby in his attack of September 4th, and forced a change in his tactics. Mosby had been wounded on September 14th and left the partisans under command of his officers. When the fighting resumed, it would be obvious to Blazer that Mosby had no intention of changing his methods.

As the fighting began again later in September 1864, both sides became involved in an event of which

While in Richmond, Mosby was promoted to full colonel on January 9, 1865. He had his picture taken in his new uniform. Notice the Union uniform in the corner. Some people say it was General Stoughton's uniform, which Mosby took when he captured him. (U.S. Army Military History Institute.)

John Munson would write: "There are some things in the lives of all of us that we can't refer to with pleasure, and the hanging and shooting of some of our men by order of General Custer ... is one of those which Mosby's men rarely refer to. Neither it, nor what followed as a result of it, are happy memories to any of us."

A group of Mosby's men under command of William Chapman was surrounded by Union troops and had to fight their way out. Amazingly, no one was killed. Six rangers, however, were taken prisoner. On September 23, 1864, General Custer "had some of them hanged and others shot with their hands tied behind their backs." Another Mosby man was executed later. To be fair, it should be noted that no one really knows whether or not it was Custer himself who ordered the executions. The rangers, based on civilian information, believed he had. Historians argue over who gave the orders. Whoever did, the rangers were executed and that led to Mosby's response.

In early November, when men from General Custer's command were captured during a raid, Mosby ordered seven of them to be hanged or shot. A note was pinned to the clothing of one victim: "These men have been hanged in retaliation for an equal number of Colonel Mosby's men hanged by order of General Custer at Front Royal. Measure for measure."

Mosby also sent a letter to Union General Philip Sheridan explaining his action and warning him: "Hereafter any prisoners falling into my hands will be treated with the kindness due to their condition, unless some new act of barbarity shall compel me reluctantly to adopt a line of policy repugnant to humanity."

Between Blazer's Scouts and direct confrontations with Union troops, the fall of 1864 had been a disaster for Mosby's operations. The rangers had been attacked themselves. For the first time ever, they had lost more men than the enemy in one engagement. Seven partisans had been executed. The men were angry and unruly, and with Mosby at home recovering, there was less control over the regiment than Mosby himself normally exercised. To make matters worse, one of the houses where Mosby stored his pistols, ammunition, and equipment was discovered by a Union raiding party, and everything was burned and destroyed. Mosby no longer was the only real force holding onto Mosby's Confederacy. It would take a determined effort on Mosby's part to bring the war in Northern Virginia back to where he was in charge.

The opportunity came on November 16, 1864, after Captain Blazer's Scouts attacked Mosby's men one time too many. Captain "Dolly" Richards, whose men had been the victims of Blazer's first successful raid in September, were given the order by Mosby to "'Wipe Blazer out!'" as John Munson remembered it. Richards set a trap for Blazer's Scouts, and Blazer walked into it. The result was a bitter fight. Ranger Alexander notes that, unlike many of the Union soldiers they surprised, Blazer's men "stood the surprise and the shock like heroes." What followed was some of the closest fighting of the rangers' careers as, in Alexander's words, "the two lines closed up ... stood horse to horse, emptying their revolvers into each other's faces." Crawford also noted the "hand-to-hand" fighting, relaying the story of Ranger Puryear, who had been a prisoner of Blazer at the beginning of the fight. As soon as his fellow rangers freed him, he "picked up a club in one hand, and with a pistol which he had borrowed, in the other, went in, knocking down on one side, and shooting on the other."

As the rout became apparent, "Blazer used every endeavor to rally his flying followers; but seeing the utter destruction of his command, and being well mounted, he endeavored to make his escape," in Williamson's words. Ranger Syd Ferguson went after him, even though he no longer had any ammunition to shoot with. As Munson tells it, "As the Captain [Blazer] did not, or could not stop, Syd knocked him from his horse as he passed by." Alexander said he used "the butt of his revolver" to do it. Blazer was taken prisoner.

Mosby and his men had regained control in Mosby's Confederacy. The Union report states only that "Two of Captain Blazer's men came in this morning ... They say that the entire command, with the exception of themselves, were either captured or killed."

The victory freed Mosby and his men from the only really successful adversaries they would encounter during the war. From now until the following April when the war ended, no one would stop them from making their attacks.

But the cause itself had by now become futile. The Confederate army and the Southern people were being worn down by the greater strength and reserves of the Union army. Mosby may have won a respite from one specific enemy, but it was becoming increasingly clear that the Union army was going to win the entire war.

Chapter 12

GUERRILLA WARFARE:
THE COST IN MEN

It's easy when looking back on Mosby and his men to see all the successes they had and to enjoy their adventures. But there is another side to life with Mosby's Rangers. There were times their raids were unsuccessful. The casualty rate among the rangers was extremely high. There was also the price paid by those civilians who hid them and fed them. These are part of the darker side of guerrilla warfare.

Ranger John Munson gave a death tally for Mosby's partisans: "During our career of a little over two years, death was making its unceasing subtractions. In that time we had seventy of our best men killed and nearly one hundred wounded. We had nine of our commissioned officers killed and nineteen of them were seriously wounded. Colonel Mosby himself was honeycombed with bullets."

Most of the memoirs written by Mosby's men tend to speak only of the successes. But James Williamson details the failures along with the successes. He wrote a detailed account of a raid in January 1864 that turned into a disaster for Mosby and his group of one hundred partisans. Mosby described the fiasco in his official report this way: "I sent Stringfellow on ahead with about 10 men to capture Major Cole and staff ... while I halted

71

to close up my command ... suddenly the party sent with Stringfellow came dashing over the hill toward the camp, yelling and shouting. They had made no attempt to secure Cole. Mistaking them for the enemy, I ordered my men to charge." Williamson wrote: "Our men supposing them to be Federals, fired upon them, killing and wounding several." In the resulting confusion, the Union captain, Captain Vernon, "rallied his men and opened on us a withering fire ... Some of the combatants stood almost in reach of one another, firing into each other's faces." As the call for reinforcements was sounded, Mosby withdrew his men, taking with him a few prisoners and many horses.

There were many unrealistic drawings made to illustrate Mosby's attacks in the newspapers and magazines of the day. The actual Mosby attacks were much more organized and precisely carried out. In many cases, men or supplies were captured in combat without any use of weapons. Sabers were never used in combat by Mosby's Rangers. (Library of Congress.)

Mosby wrote in his report: "My loss was severe; more so in the worth than the number slain." The rangers had left four dead; four others would die from their wounds. The enemy had lost five killed. Williamson described their march home as "gloomy" and with a "sad and sullen silence." He notes that Mosby "though he usually appeared cold and unyielding, could not conceal his disappointment and keen regret at the result of this enterprise."

This would be one of their worst failures, and the relatively large loss of men was very unusual for a Mosby attack. It probably is important to note in passing that this particular raid was not planned by Mosby, as most raids were. Captain Stringfellow was one of General Stuart's scouts. He came to Mosby with information he had obtained about the Union camp and convinced him a successful raid was possible. What this disaster may prove is that Mosby was most effective when he did his own planning based on his own information.

It was important that Mosby protect his soldiers because his command was small in numbers. Any losses would seem large. His men trusted his fighting instincts. John Alexander remembered Mosby as a "wily as well as daring fighter," who "never let his valor get the better of his discretion — at least, not in the handling of his men. He always sought to secure for them every possible advantage for a fight, and his almost unvarying success in this was one of the marks of his genius."

No matter the care and planning, the losses and danger ran high. Mosby himself was wounded seven times. One historian puts the casualty rate for Mosby's men at thirty-five to forty percent of the command, which is an incredibly high number. John Munson boasted "our little command in two years lost more men killed, wounded, and captured, and more officers killed and wounded, than any full cavalry regiment during the entire four years of the war, and we were in more fights, big and little, during our two years of existence, than any cavalry or infantry regiment in the army." He continued, justifying the boast with this further comment: "Our loss in killed and wounded in nearly every fight was much less, proportionately to the number of men on both sides than the enemy's." It is interesting that, writing years after the war, Munson still felt that the nature of their warfare and the damage they did justified the losses they had. All the other rangers who wrote memoirs would probably agree. They had lived through the day-to-day risk and felt the fight was worth it.

It is hard to say whether they were right or wrong so many years later. But it is important to note that they knew the risks and freely chose to be part of Mosby's partisan fighters. However, there were others who became part of the fighting whether they chose to or not. These were the civilians living in Mosby's Confederacy. For them, their very homes and fields became a battle-ground.

Chapter 13

GUERRILLA WARFARE:
THE COST TO THE CIVILIANS

I *have read of civilized warfare, but that was not the kind the invaders waged against the defenseless inhabitants of Fauquier ... The cruelties and atrocities of the barbarous foe inspired our partisan soldiers with more than human courage.* These words written by Dr. Monteiro show how strongly the rangers reacted to revenge by Union troops against Mosby's civilian supporters. It is not surprising that Mosby's men would react this way. It is also not surprising that the Union would have taken action against the people aiding Mosby's work.

The issue of how civilians should be treated when they house and aid an enemy was not new to the Civil War. As an issue, it still exists today. What made it such an important issue at the time was the feelings of people on both sides about guerrilla warfare. The Union reaction to what they perceived as the Confederates not playing fair was at first very military and correct. Over time, however, as Mosby's partisans continued to harass them, they grew impatient. It was almost inevitable that at some time they would decide their only solution lay in scaring the civilian population into submission.

One area in which the Union was suffering a great deal of damage was their supply trains. As Mosby and his men repeatedly attacked and derailed the trains, the

Mosby and his wife bought this home in Warrenton, Virginia, after the Civil War. During the war, Pauline often joined him at one of the "safe houses" located in Mosby's Confederacy. (Library of Congress.)

Union leadership devised a unique form of "insurance" for their trains. Mosby wrote to General Lee on October 29, 1864 to tell him of the Union response to his attacks: "In retaliation they arrested a large number of citizens living along the lines, and have been in the habit of sending an installment of them on each train." He asks Lee for some action: "As my command has done nothing contrary to the usages of war, it seems to me that some attempt at least ought to be made to prevent a repetition of such barbarities."

Ranger Major John Scott described these Union actions as "inhuman." He had less of a problem with the fact that captured rangers were also put on the trains. He also describes Mosby's decision to continue attacking the trains: "With the spirit of an old Roman, Mosby declared, 'If my wife and children were on board, I would still throw off the cars.'"

The ultimate revenge of the Union troops on the civilian population came when General David Hunter took over command of the Union troops in the area. In May 1864, General Hunter issued an official proclamation that included the decision: "For every train fired or soldier assassinated, the house and other property of every secession sympathizer residing within a circuit of five miles shall be destroyed by fire."

The reaction of Mosby's men was bitter. Williamson wrote, "These citizens upon whom Hunter proposed to retaliate were no more responsible for our acts than the most loyal citizens of the North, and they were powerless to prevent them."

Ranger Munson described his reaction on coming upon the first victims of General Hunter's wrath: "The entreaties of the women and children had been of no avail ... The sight of those helpless non-combatants crouching in the rain, weeping over their burning homes, wrought up the resentment of the men ... Our men were demons that day."

Mosby had a more coolly logical response. When his men captured one of the soldiers firing the buildings, he executed him. Major Scott said that "Mosby then dispatched a letter to the Federal commander in the Valley ... and a declaration that he would continue to have all house-burners executed who might fall into his hands."

In November 1864, all of Loudoun County felt the hand of Union revenge. Union General Philip H. Sheridan's orders to Major-General Wesley Merritt, dated November 27, are clear: "To clear the country of these parties that are bringing destruction upon the innocent as well as their guilty supporters by their cowardly acts, you will consume and destroy all forage and subsistence, burn all barns and mills and their contents, and drive off all stock in the region ... This order must be literally executed." Sheridan justified his orders: "The ultimate results of the guerrilla system of warfare is the total destruction of all private rights in the country occupied by such parties ... the responsibility of it must rest upon the authorities at Richmond, who have acknowledged the legitimacy of guerrilla bands." For the next five days, the Union troops carried out Sheridan's orders to the letter.

It is horrible reading the accounts of these raids against the civilians. The issue of whether Mosby's actions justified this harm to the civilians and whether this damage could have been prevented is still argued by historians today.

There is no question that Mosby and his men felt their form of warfare was legal and fair. Mosby wrote: "The complaints against us did not recognize the fact that there are two parties of equal right in a war. The error men make is in judging conduct in war by the standards of peace." There is also no doubt the Union leadership felt that partisans in general, and Mosby in particular, were not fighting by the accepted rules of warfare. Thus they felt that taking action against Mosby's civilian supporters was a justified response to the situation.

No matter which side was right, the horrible fact is that civilian noncombatants found themselves burned out of their homes and farms simply for living in an area where Mosby chose to stage raids.

Chapter 14

FAMOUS (AND NOT SO FAMOUS) RANGERS

Mosby frequently divided his men into small detachments, each under a competent officer ... through his excellent judgment of men, he had surrounded himself with officers for the different companies in whom he could place implicit confidence in carrying out his orders. These words of John Munson make a good introduction to some stories about Mosby's most famous rangers.

Mosby, no matter how brilliant a strategist, no matter how personally daring, could not have been the success he was without the men he selected for his command. Their stories all joined together are what make up his stories. Munson himself gives the example of Ned Hurst, who was part of the original group of fifteen men Mosby selected under Stuart's orders. Munson says Hurst was involved in just about every fight they were in and "was wounded seven times, twice in one fight ... he was often in his saddle when he ought to have been in bed. He thought he was safer in his saddle." Hurst reportedly killed over one hundred Union soldiers during his two-year career with the rangers.

There are all sorts of numbers for how many rangers there were, from 500 to over 2,000. Even if there were only a few, it would be impossible to tell the story of each

Mosby (sitting in center) with some of his rangers. (U.S. Army Military History Institute.)

one here. But some of the stories just have to be told.

Mosby himself chose to remember John Underwood of Fairfax County, Virginia. Also one of the original rangers, Mosby wrote of him: "I was largely indebted to his skill and intelligence for whatever success I had in the beginning of my partisan life. He was killed a few months afterward, and I never found his like again."

Two brothers, Sam and William Chapman, both became officers in Mosby's command. William became a major and, by the end of the war, led one of the two battalions in Mosby's regiment. Sam was known as the "fighting parson." John Alexander remembered that "the Reverend Chapman considered that Mosby's men were organized for fighting purposes; that whenever Providence presented an opportunity for a fight it was his simple duty to embrace it and trust the Lord for consequences."

Both Chapman brothers had reputations as "savage" fighters. In some ways, they — especially Sam — were more daring than Mosby. Mosby remembered a very difficult fight where, in a desperate attempt to allow the other men to escape, Sam Chapman and a few others set up their small howitzer to guard the rear. Mosby wrote that Chapman and company "had never looked so happy in their lives. As for myself, realizing the desperate straits we were in, I wished I was somewhere else."

One of Mosby's most famous officers was Adolphus "Dolly" Richards. Dolly Richards gained fame for escaping from a house surrounded by Union troops by jumping from a second-story window and shooting his way out. Mosby appreciated his courage, and by the end of the war Dolly was a major in command of three companies of men (300-400 men) and was operating independently of Mosby himself.

The men were devoted to each other. John Munson told a story of being wounded and having an unknown ranger save him: "One of our men reached out and held me on my horse ... succeeded in getting me into a nearby house and placing me on a lounge, after which he rushed off to finish his engagement with the Yankees ... my friend never thought enough of the incident to look me up later and receive my thanks." There are many stories such as this one that show the bond among the men and their loyalty not only to Mosby but to each other as well.

Some of the men had a devotion to duty that was almost unbelievable. John Munson remembers Charley Wiltshire, one of two brothers from the Valley of Virginia, who served with Mosby. Charley had served in the regular Confederate army and had been wounded several times. He was finally discharged as unfit to fight. Munson notes that "he began his guerrilla tactics when he should have been in the hospital." Charley found himself in a difficult situation on his first venture as a ranger and, not having a weapon available, "broke his crutch over a Federal soldier's head."

The rangers came to Mosby's command in many different ways. There's the story of how Henry Cabell "Cab" Maddux joined the rangers. One day Union troops were advancing into Mosby territory past Upperville, Virginia. Mosby and his men responded by attacking the Union troops and then chasing them back through Upperville. Munson remembers that as they drove the troops through Upperville, a fourteen-year-old boy was outside school at recess. He saw the rangers, grabbed a horse, and followed them out of town. He didn't return to school and instead became a ranger.

Mosby's own younger brother, Willie, joined the rangers in 1863 at the age of eighteen. Dr. Monteiro tells of one of his own first nights with the rangers. Before calmly going to sleep, Willie Mosby advised him "that our headquarters were liable to be attacked at any hour; the enemy had recently made a raid on it; they always attacked at night, and that our chances of escape consisted in being well armed and either escape at one door as they broke through another, or cut our way through the columns that surrounded the house as they frequently did." Dr. Monteiro did not sleep easily that night, but Willie seemed totally unbothered by the threat.

The stories of heroism seem endless. James Williamson tells the one of Ranger William R. Stone, "struck on the head with a carbine and left for dead on the field." When he recovered consciousness, he washed the blood from his face and searched around, finding another ranger, named Yates, wounded and thought to be dead. Rousing him, the two of them located a third companion, made a litter to carry him, and "proceeded to a place of safety." This incident, surely heroic enough for most people, rates only one short paragraph in one of the memoirs. It received no special comment apparently because it was regarded as an event that was simply part of the routine life of the rangers.

Then there is the story of John Atkins, who heard of Mosby's exploits while still in Ireland and "left home and country to join his fortune with ours," in the words of Williamson. He would die from wounds suffered in a raid. Williamson praised him as "brave, generous, of good education, agreeable in his manner," and noted that he "had in the short time he was with us made many friends."

The stories are endless. In trying to pick the ones to share here, something written by Ranger John Munson in his reminiscences seemed to sum up the difficulty in choosing just a few stories: "I would like to tell of some individual act of each man in the Command, and record the hundreds of brave deeds I witnessed or knew of, but I can only repeat what I once heard Mosby say when he was writing one of his reports to General Stuart." Finding that Mosby had listed his own name as deserving credit in a recent raid, Munson asked why not others. Mosby replied, "'I can't call the roll in every fight, Munson.'"

Chapter 15

IN THE END, AGAIN

Today there is a group of people who are dedicated to the task of making sure everyone remembers the accomplishments of Mosby and his rangers. In 1983, the Stuart-Mosby Society was founded to honor the memories of Mosby and Confederate General J.E.B. Stuart, under whom Mosby began his scouting career. It is appropriate that they be remembered together as it was Stuart who encouraged and supported the work of the partisans. Adele Mitchell, one of the founders of the organization, when asked why there is a need for this group, replied that she felt "it was time they [Mosby and Stuart] get recognition not only for their achievements but also for their character." Mosby, she said, was a "wonderful example of honor and loyalty and achievement. He was never engaged in anything bad."

Members of the organization, which include Mosby's grandson, a retired admiral, and General Stuart's namesake, Colonel J.E.B. Stuart, IV (who is president of the organization), meet for special memorial ceremonies and to research the lives of both men. They also fiercely defend the reputation of these Confederate leaders, responding to any printed attack on their character or military leadership, both in their own publication, *Southern Cavalry Review*, and elsewhere. For this group of 350 people, the Civil War and Mosby's adventures are memories to be treasured.

The Fifth Reunion of the 43rd Battalion took place in 1898. Mosby himself did not attend the reunions, but two of his daughters were present at this one. (University of Virginia Library.)

Mosby has needed his defenders. He remains one of the most controversial figures of the Civil War. There is still an ongoing debate about his tactics. People still question whether or not the way he fought was an honorable one.

Mosby's choice of partisan guerrilla warfare resulted in criticism from the very beginning. Both the Union and Confederate armies began the Civil War with the romantic notion that war was an honorable and glorious venture. By the end of the war, the horror of war had mostly destroyed its romantic image. Stories from the war include reminiscences of soldiers from both sides sharing tobacco and food in the evening, and then facing each other as enemies the following morning. From this view of fighting, guerrilla warfare seemed somehow dishonorable and not worthy of the "real" soldier. There was also an image that guerrillas were all people who would never have been considered morally good enough to be allowed to fight in the regular army. They were seen as plunderers, fighting not for the cause, but for their own personal gain. Ranger Munson's memoir answered that charge this way: "Mosby's Guerrillas were not highwayman, bushwhackers or ruffians, and that they did not war upon any element other than that commonly recognized as the enemy. A very large percentage of them were well-bred, refined gentlemen ... They were men of firm convictions, for which they were anxious to fight and willing to make sacrifices."

It is also important to realize that Mosby was not the only partisan leader of the war. He was simply the most effective one. The Confederate leaders had not wanted to have partisan soldiers fighting for their cause at first. But there was great pressure for these groups among the Confederate citizens themselves. In April 1862, the Confederate Congress passed the Partisan Ranger Act, allowing the formation of partisan groups. Six months later (before Mosby's group was organized), other partisan groups were already at work in many areas in the South. Mosby was by no means the only partisan leader, but he is certainly the most remembered.

Mosby is remembered both for the success of his operations and also because his operations occurred in an area that caused the maximum fear for Union leaders and civilians. The Union troops could never feel totally secure as long as he was operating in their area.

Mosby added to that fear with the boldness of his operations. History gives us reports by Mosby of raid after raid involving only twenty to thirty rangers who sneak into a camp and capture men and horses without even disturbing the sleeping soldiers in the camp. Mosby's use of stealth, his attacks at night, his ability to do just enough damage without trying to be greedy — all this earned him and his rangers a reputation much more glorious and fearsome than the actual results of his raids would indicate. The effect of his strategies can be seen over and over again in the Union reports in the *Official Record*, which exaggerated how many men were involved in the attacks. Mosby succeeded in creating and maintaining an atmosphere of fear for the Union command in all of Northern Virginia.

The guerrilla warfare that Mosby conducted was not really strategically important in the Civil War. But psychologically his impact on the Union leadership went far beyond any actual damage he caused. The Union forces in Northern Virginia were spread out over a large area, and they never knew when or where Mosby and his rangers would strike next. Mosby set out "to threaten and harass the enemy on the border." He was very successful in achieving his goal.

For a Confederate cause that lost and for a people who had to accept the defeat, Mosby would remain a shining example of the times they were successful. In his final address to his command, Mosby would strike the same defiant tone as ever: "The vision we cherished of a free and independent country has vanished, and that country is now the spoil of a conqueror. I disband your organization in preference to surrendering to our enemies ... I part from you with a just pride in the fame of your achievements."

The image is strong — Mosby, the unbeaten, refusing to surrender to the Union forces even after Confederate General Lee surrendered at Appomattox Court House. Mosby, the defender of the area known as Mosby's Confederacy, passed from Southern hero into Southern legend, a sweet memory for a nation defeated in an otherwise bitter war.

SOURCES FOR RESEARCH

The story of Mosby and his partisan band is an interesting one. It is also one about which there is much disagreement. I wanted to tell the story of the rangers as an adventure story. I wanted to capture the excitement of their fighting in their own words. To do this, I went back to Mosby's own memoirs and those of several of his men. I also read Mosby's letters at the University of Virginia, the Library of Congress, and the United States Military History Institute, as well as those included in a collection of his letters published by the Stuart-Mosby Historical Society.

It is important for my readers to understand that because this book is written through the words of Mosby and his men, it mostly presents only one side of the story. In several chapters, I have tried to give you a sense of the darker side so that you would see there was indeed a dark side to partisan warfare. Mostly, however, you are seeing the Mosby known as the "Gray Ghost" — a very heroic, legendary figure of the Civil War.

Mosby himself left two memoirs. The first is *Mosby's War Reminiscences and Stuart's Cavalry Campaigns* (Boston: George A. Jones & Co., 1887). The second is *The Memoirs of Colonel John S. Mosby* (edited by Charles Wells Russell, Boston: Little, Brown, and Company, 1917). I have also used the memoirs of several of Mosby's men: John H. Alexander's *Mosby's Men* (New York: The

Neale Publishing Company, 1907); J. Marshall Crawford's *Mosby and His Men* (New York: G.W. Carleton & Co., 1867); Dr. Aristides Monteiro's *War Reminiscences by the Surgeon of Mosby's Command* (Richmond, Virginia: privately published, 1890); John W. Munson's *Reminiscences of a Mosby Guerrilla* (New York: Moffat, Yard and Company, 1906); Adolphus E. Richards' "Mosby's 'Partizan Rangers,' in *Famous Adventures and Prison Escapes of the Civil War* (New York: The Century Co., 1893); Major John Scott's *Partisan Life with Colonel John S. Mosby* (New York: Harper & Brothers, 1867); and James J. Williamson's *Mosby's Rangers* (New York: Sturgis & Walton Company, 1909). Whenever I refer to an official report, the information comes from *The War of the Rebellion: A Compilation of the Official Records of the Union and Confederate Armies* , published in 128 volumes by the U.S. Government Printing Office in the late 1800s.

I always read several background books on a subject before beginning research. There have been many books published on Mosby. I will mention four that I think present the most balanced view of his life and career. Virgil Carrington Jones wrote two: *Ranger Mosby* (Chapel Hill, North Carolina: University of North Carolina Press, 1944) and *Gray Ghosts and Rebel Raiders* (New York: Henry Holt and Company, 1956). Two newer biographies are Kevin H. Siepel's *Rebel: The Life and Times of John Singleton Mosby* (New York: St. Martin's Press, 1983) and Jeffrey D. Wert's *Mosby's Rangers* (New York: Simon and Schuster, 1990).

INDEX